Fit &

Fashionable

800 Coco Drive, Coconut Grove, FL 33133

INSTRUCTIONS FOR USING BUSINESS FORMS

This booklet contains Forms 1 through 61. Use these forms as the source of information for journalizing the transactions. The forms are perforated in order that they may be removed as you analyze and record the transactions. When you remove them, place the edge of a ruler on the perforation and tear carefully. Otherwise the forms may be damaged.

Remember to post daily to the subsidiary ledgers if you are working the practice set manually. After you have journalized a transaction, file the related business form in one of the files provided in this set. The files are as follows:

Title of File	Materials to Be Filed
Checks Received	Checks received
Sales Invoices	Accounting Department copy of sales invoices and credit memos issued by the business
Purchase Invoices	Unpaid purchase invoices and credit memos received from vendors
Outgoing Papers	Checks deposited and accompanying deposit tickets
Office File	Paid purchase invoices; interoffice communications; duplicate checks; duplicate deposit tickets

Date of Entries

It is the custom of the business to have each piece of incoming mail stamped to show the date on which it was received. All transactions represented by incoming paper are to be recorded not according to the dates on which the papers were written, but according to the dates on which the papers were received by the business.

Sales and Purchases

Each sale is evidenced by a copy of the sales invoice marked "Accounting Department Copy." Each purchase is evidenced by a purchase invoice. Record purchases at the gross amount. Record any purchase discounts at the time of the payment, and deduct the amount of the discount from merchandise inventory.

Checkbook

All cash payments are made by check. Record the beginning cash balance in the checkbook provided, and keep a continuous checkbook cash balance if you are working the practice set manually. The checks are prenumbered starting with #2201.

Form 2. All sales on account are made on terms of 2/10, n/30. Record the Cost of Merchandise Sold, as noted on the copy.

Form 13. The total amount of cash received from cash sales for April 1–6 has been deposited in the bank by Mr. Chavez. On April 6 you receive Form 13, a duplicate of the deposit ticket for this deposit, from which you are to record the cash sales for the week and the cost of merchandise sold. Make the proper journal entry to record the total cash sales represented by the duplicate deposit ticket. Also, for the manual practice set, be sure to record the amount of the deposit on the proper check stub in the checkbook. Follow this procedure each time you receive a deposit ticket marked "Copy."

Form 14, April 6. Fill out the deposit ticket and deposit all checks on hand. If you are working the manual practice set, record the amount of the deposit on the check stub in your checkbook immediately below the cash sales deposit. The completed deposit ticket, together with all checks being deposited, should be filed in the Outgoing Papers file. The same procedure should be followed for Form 29 on April 13, Form 44 on April 20, and Form 61 on April 30.

Form 20, April 9. Fit & Fashionable records all sales returns and purchase returns in the general journal.

Posting to the General Ledger

Follow the instructions contained in Booklet 1.

Form 1

Alexus Fitness Connection
100 Coral Way
Miami, FL 33129

REC'D April 01

Date March 29, 20--

Shipped Via Boyd Trucking
Terms Net 30
Invoice No. 1652

Sold To Fit & Fashionable
800 Coco Drive
Coconut Grove, FL 33133

Quantity	Description	Unit Price	Amount
20	Sports Bag	12.00	240.00
25	Treadmill I	500.00	12,500.00
5	Cycling Bike I	225.00	1,125.00
	TOTAL		13,865.00

Form 2

Fit & Fashionable

800 Coco Drive, Coconut Grove, FL 33133

Date: 4/1/20--
Invoice: 301
Shipped Via: Express Trucking
Terms: 2/10, n/30
Sold To: Miami Health Club
8050 S.W. 8th Street
Miami, FL 33130

Quantity	Item	Unit Cost	Amount
10	Heart Rate Pocket Monitor	56.25	562.50
1	Spin Bike IV	3,360.00	3,360.00
2	Cycling Bike I	315.75	631.50
20	Cycling Shorts	42.79	855.80
	Total		5,409.80

Record all credit sales at net amount MC

Accounting Department Copy — For Office Use Only

Cost of Merchandise Sold 3,864.00	Sale net of 2% discount 5,301.60

Form 3

Fit & Fashionable

800 Coco Drive, Coconut Grove, FL 33133

Interoffice Memo

To: Bookkeeper **Date:** April 1, 20--

Please issue a check for $14,268.80 to Alexus Fitness Connection in payment of its invoice of March 6.

Marty Chavez

Form 4

Body Excellence Fitness Club
9 Key Biscayne Ave., Suite 100
Key Biscayne, FL 33149

REC'D April 02

202

April 1 20 --

PAY TO THE ORDER OF Fit & Fashionable $ 14,406.00

Fourteen thousand, four hundred six and 00/100------------ **Dollars**

(For Classroom Use Only)

NATIONAL SAVINGS

For 3/27 Inv. Less 2% Discount

Matt Newberry

⑆ 566 780001⑆ 551⑈1⑈ 0202

Fit &

Fashionable

800 Coco Drive, Coconut Grove, FL 33133

Form 5

Interoffice Memo

To: Bookkeeper **Date:** April 2, 20--

Please issue a check for $5,700.00 to Harvey Insurance Company as a prepayment of insurance for a 12-month policy.

Marty Chavez

Fit &

Fashionable

800 Coco Drive, Coconut Grove, FL 33133

Form 6

Interoffice Memo

To: Bookkeeper **Date:** April 3, 20--

Please issue a check for $46,480.00 to Fizzy-Cal Network in payment of its invoice of March 7.

Marty Chavez

Form 7

Fit & Fashionable

800 Coco Drive, Coconut Grove, FL 33133

Date: 4/3/20--
Invoice: 302
Shipped Via: Speedy Trucking

Terms: 2/10, n/30

Sold To: All Access Fitness Centers
1 South Park Blvd.
South Miami, FL 33143

Quantity	Item	Unit Cost	Amount
2	Exercise Bike Advanced	1,025.00	2,050.00
10	Unisex DryFit Shirt	33.60	336.00
6	Warmup Suit	74.90	449.40
2	Spin Bike II	3,360.00	6,720.00
	Total		9,555.40

Accounting Department Copy — For Office Use Only

Cost of Merchandise Sold 6,825.00	*Sale net of 2% discount 9,364.29*

Form 8

Cory's Gym in the Grove
20 Main Highway
Coconut Grove, FL 33133

REC'D April 03

555

April 2 20 --

Pay to the Order of Fit & Fashionable $ 12,348.00

Twelve thousand, three hundred forty-eight and 00/100----- **Dollars**

(For Classroom Use Only)

BANKER'S TRUST OF MIAMI

For 3/27 Inv. Less 2% Discount

Cory Stewart

⑆ 01 822205⑆ 990⑈ 2⑈ 0555

Form 9

Fit &
& Fashionable

800 Coco Drive, Coconut Grove, FL 33133

Interoffice Memo

To: Bookkeeper **Date:** April 4, 20--

Please issue a check for $14,000.00 to HeartFit Enterprises in payment of its invoice of March 8.

Marty Chavez

Form 10

The Sun Set
Recreation Centers
50 Snapper Creek Dr.
Sunset, FL 33173

REC'D April 04

4508

April 3 20 --

Pay to the Order of Fit & Fashionable **$** 6,174.00

Six thousand, one hundred seventy-four and 00/100--------- **Dollars**

(For Classroom Use Only)

LINCOLN FEDERAL SAVINGS BANK

For 3/28 Inv. Less 2% Discount *Chris E. Lee*

⑆ 900 002230⑆ 25⑈011⑈ 4508

Form 11

Fit & Fashionable

800 Coco Drive, Coconut Grove, FL 33133

Date: 4/5/20--
Invoice: 303
Shipped Via: Express Trucking

Terms: 2/10, n/30

Sold To: Westwood Boxing Gym
50 Westwood Lake Dr.
Miami, FL 33165

Quantity	Item	Unit Cost	Amount
5	Spin Bike III	3,920.00	19,600.00
5	Treadmill I	781.25	3,906.25
10	Cycling Bike II	393.75	3,937.50
25	Sports Bag	16.80	420.00
	Total		27,863.75

Accounting Department Copy — For Office Use Only

Cost of Merchandise Sold	*Sale net of 2% discount*
19,903.68	*27,306.48*

Form 12

Sports Magic Warehouse

246 Santa Monica Blvd.
Santa Monica, CA 90403

REC'D April 05

Shipped Via Our Truck
Terms Net 30
Invoice No. 243

Date April 4, 20--
Sold To Fit & Fashionable
800 Coco Drive
Coconut Grove, FL 33133

Quantity	Description	Unit Price	Amount
10	Spin Bike Lubricator	20.00	200.00
10	Spin Bike I	2,000.00	20,000.00
5	Spin Bike II	2,400.00	12,000.00
5	Spin Bike III	2,800.00	14,000.00
50	Unisex DryFit Shirt	24.00	1,200.00
25	Cycling Shorts	42.79	1,069.75
	Freight Charges F.O.B. Shipping Point		1,050.00
	Total		49,519.75

Form 13

South Miami Bank

63-22
631

Date April 6, 20--

Fit &
& Fashionable
800 Coco Drive, Coconut Grove, FL 33133

Cost of Merchandise Sold $18,024.00

⑆ 74 002044⑆ 2⑈099 1⑈

COPY

	$	Cents
Cash	23,200	00
Checks 94-101	542	50
74-89	755	80
101-89	1,245	00
94-55	682	70
72-88	174	00
Cash Sales		
April 1-6		
Total	26,600	00

Form 14

South Miami Bank

63-22
631

Date

Fit &
Fashionable
800 Coco Drive, Coconut Grove, FL 33133

⑆ 74 002044⑆ 2⑈099 1⑈

	$	Cents
Cash		
Checks		
Total		

Form 15

Westwood Boxing Gym
50 Westwood Lake Dr.
Miami, FL 33165

REC'D April 08

3806

April 7 20 --

Pay to the Order of Fit & Fashionable $ 8,232.00

Eight thousand, two hundred thirty-two and 00/100--------- **Dollars**

(For Classroom Use Only)

CENTRAL SAVINGS

For 3/29 Inv. Less 2% Discount

Lamar Harris

⑆ 770 003991⑆ 220⑈116⑈ 3806

Form 16

Fit & Fab Health Products
15 Park Avenue, 115th Floor
New York, NY 10154

REC'D April 08

Date April 6, 20--

Shipped Via Boyd Trucking
Terms 2/10, n/30
Invoice No. 426

Sold To Fit & Fashionable
800 Coco Drive
Coconut Grove, FL 33133

Quantity	Description	Unit Price	Amount
12	Rowing Kit Portable	90.00	1,080.00
10	Rowing Kit Pro	380.00	3,800.00
10	Rowing Gloves Leather	35.00	350.00
	TOTAL		5,230.00

Record this invoice at the amount net of the discount, or $5,125.40
MC

Form 17

Fit & Fashionable

800 Coco Drive, Coconut Grove, FL 33133

Date: 4/8/20-- **Terms:** 2/10, n/30 **Sold To:** The Sun Set Rec. Centers
Invoice: 304 50 Snapper Creek Dr.
Shipped Via: Overland Express Sunset, FL 33173

Quantity	Item	Unit Cost	Amount
6	Exercise Bike	840.00	5,040.00
10	Jogging Stroller	184.80	1,848.00
3	Spin Bike III	3,920.00	11,760.00
100	Spin Bike Lubricator	31.25	3,125.00
10	Cycling Shorts	42.79	427.90
	Total		22,200.90

Accounting Department Copy — For Office Use Only

Cost of Merchandise Sold 15,858.00	*Sale net of 2% discount 21,756.88*

Form 18

Pine Bay Fitness Club
8 SW 57th Ave.
Miami, FL 33156

REC'D April 08

2719

April 5 20 --

PAY TO THE ORDER OF Fit & Fashionable **$** 10,976.00

Ten thousand, nine hundred seventy-six and 00/100--------- **Dollars**

(For Classroom Use Only)

CENTRAL BANK & TRUST

For 3/30 Inv. Less 2% Discount

Lisa Walters

⑆ 79 83000⑆ 2⑈0116⑈ 2719

Form 19

FIZZY-CAL NETWORK
45 Caribbean Avenue
Los Angeles, CA 90001

REC'D April 09

DATE: April 8, 20--

SOLD TO: Fit & Fashionable
800 Coco Drive
Coconut Grove, FL 33133

INVOICE NO.: 1693
SHIPPED VIA: Carriage Trucking
TERMS: Net 30

QUANTITY	DESCRIPTION	UNIT PRICE	AMOUNT
10	Exercise Bike	600.00	6,000.00
5	Exercise Bike Advanced	720.00	3,600.00
1	Custom Store Display	1,800.00	1,800.00
	Charge to Store Supplies	**TOTAL**	11,400.00

Form 20

Fit & Fashionable

800 Coco Drive, Coconut Grove, FL 33133

CREDIT MEMO NO. 107

Date: 4/9/20--
For: Our Invoice of April 8
We credit your account as follows:

Sold To: The Sun Set Rec. Centers
50 Snapper Creek Dr.
Sunset, FL 33173

Quantity	Item	Unit Cost	Amount
1	Exercise Bike	840.00	840.00
	Total		840.00

Accounting Department Copy — For Office Use Only

Cost of Merchandise Sold 600.00 | *Sale net of 2% discount 823.20*

Form 21

Fit & Fashionable

800 Coco Drive, Coconut Grove, FL 33133

Interoffice Memo

To: Bookkeeper **Date:** April 10, 20--

Please issue a check to me for $175.00 for entertaining a customer. Charge to Miscellaneous Selling Expense.

Marty Chavez

Form 22

Fit & Fashionable

800 Coco Drive, Coconut Grove, FL 33133

Date: 4/10/20-- **Terms:** 2/10, n/30 **Sold To:** Rockdale Gym
Invoice: 305 162 S. Dixie Hwy.
Shipped Via: Express Trucking Rockdale, FL 33157

Quantity	Item	Unit Cost	Amount
4	Rowing Gloves Leather	49.50	198.00
4	Rowing Kit Pro	565.00	2,260.00
3	Spin Bike IV	3,360.00	10,080.00
6	Jogging Stroller	184.80	1,108.80
	Total		13,646.80

Accounting Department Copy — For Office Use Only

Cost of Merchandise Sold 9,412.00 | *Sale net of 2% discount 13,373.86*

Form 23

Fit & Fab Health Products
15 Park Avenue, 115th Floor
New York, NY 10154

REC'D April 11

CREDIT MEMO

Date April 10, 20--

Sold To Fit & Fashionable
800 Coco Drive
Coconut Grove, FL 33133

CM No. 432 On our invoice dated April 6, 20--

Quantity	Description	Unit Price	Amount
7	Rowing Kit Portable	90.00	630.00
7	Rowing Gloves Leather	35.00	245.00
	TOTAL	*Record at discounted amount of $857.50 MC*	875.00

Form 24

SupplyMax
5 Bird Road
Miami, FL 33155

REC'D April 11

1102

April 10 20 --

Pay to the Order of Fit & Fashionable $ 300.00

Three hundred and 00/100---------------------------------- **Dollars**

(For Classroom Use Only)

Southeastern Savings

For Returned Store Supplies Toni Roddi

⑆ 88 300448⑆ 333⑈006⑈ 1102

Form 25

Miami Health Club
8050 S.W. 8th Street
Miami, FL 33130

REC'D April 11

2599

April 10 20 --

Pay to the Order of Fit & Fashionable $ 5,301.60

Five thousand, three hundred one and 60/100-------------- **Dollars**

(For Classroom Use Only)

COLUMBIA SAVINGS

For 4/1 Inv. #301 Less 2% Discount

Dan Riley

⑆ 7 808330⑆ 5⑈0001⑈ 2599

Form 26

All Access Fitness Centers
1 South Park Blvd.
South Miami, FL 33143

REC'D April 12

465

April 12 20 --

Pay to the Order of Fit & Fashionable $ 9,364.29

Nine thousand, three hundred sixty-four and 29/100------- **Dollars**

(For Classroom Use Only)

COLUMBIA SAVINGS

For 4/3 Inv. #302 Less 2% Discount

Ann Goldberg

⑆ 76 22144⑆ 333⑈07⑈ 0465

Form 27

Fit &

& Fashionable

800 Coco Drive, Coconut Grove, FL 33133

Interoffice Memo

To: Bookkeeper **Date:** April 13, 20--

Please issue a check to Payroll for $13,000 for biweekly salaries: Sales Salaries, $8,000; Office Salaries, $5,000.

Marty Chavez

Form 28

South Miami Bank

63-22
631

Date April 13, 20--

Fit &

Fashionable

800 Coco Drive, Coconut Grove, FL 33133

Cost of Merchandise Sold $24,910.80

⑆ 74 002044⑆ 2⑈099 1⑈

COPY

		$	Cents
Cash		28,700	00
Checks	92-04	1,650	00
	104-20	5,770	00
Cash Sales			
April 8-13			
	Total	36,120	00

Form 29

South Miami Bank

63-22
631

Date ______________________

	$	Cents
Cash		
Checks		
Total		

Fit &

& Fashionable

800 Coco Drive, Coconut Grove, FL 33133

⑆ 74 002044⑆ 2⑈099 1⑈

Form 30

Westwood Boxing Gym
50 Westwood Lake Dr.
Miami, FL 33165

REC'D April 15

3996

April 12 20 --

Pay to the Order of Fit & Fashionable **$** 27,306.48

Twenty-seven thousand, three hundred six and 48/100------ **Dollars**

(For Classroom Use Only)

CENTRAL SAVINGS

For 4/5 Inv. #303 Less 2% Discount

Lamar Harris

⑆ 770 003991⑆ 220⑈116⑈ 3806

Form 31

Alexus Fitness Connection
100 Coral Way
Miami, FL 33129

REC'D April 16

Date April 14, 20--

Shipped Via Boyd Trucking
Terms Net 30
Invoice No. 1725

Sold To Fit & Fashionable
800 Coco Drive
Coconut Grove, FL 33133

Quantity	Description	Unit Price	Amount
25	Jogging Stroller	132.00	3,300.00
15	Cycling Bike II	252.00	3,780.00
25	Jogging Suit	84.00	2,100.00
1	Promotion Pack	250.00	250.00
10	Display Cases	67.50	675.00
	TOTAL		10,105.00

Charge to Store Supplies (250.00)

Charge to Miscellaneous Selling Expense (675.00)

Form 32

Fit & Fashionable

800 Coco Drive, Coconut Grove, FL 33133

Date: 4/16/20--
Invoice: 306
Shipped Via: Express Trucking

Terms: 2/10, n/30

Sold To: Miami Health Club
8050 SW 8th Street
Miami, FL 33130

Quantity	Item	Unit Cost	Amount
2	Rowing Kit Pro	565.00	1,130.00
17	Running Shorts	42.50	722.50
1	Stair Climber Pro	3,375.00	3,375.00
16	Unisex DryFit Shirts	33.60	537.60
	Total		5,765.10

Accounting Department Copy — For Office Use Only

Cost of Merchandise Sold 4,115.20	*Sale net of 2% discount 5,649.80*

Form 33

Fit & Fashionable

800 Coco Drive, Coconut Grove, FL 33133

Interoffice Memo

To: Bookkeeper **Date:** April 17, 20--

Please issue me a check for $4,200.00 for personal use.

Marty Chavez

Form 34

Fit & Fashionable

800 Coco Drive, Coconut Grove, FL 33133

Interoffice Memo

To: Bookkeeper **Date:** April 17, 20--

Please issue a check for $441.00 to *U.S. Health & Fitness Magazine* for an advertisement.

Marty Chavez

Form 35

Sports Magic Warehouse
246 Santa Monica Blvd.
Santa Monica, CA 90403

REC'D April 17

Shipped Via	Our Truck	*Date*	April 16, 20--
Terms	Net 30	*Sold To*	Fit & Fashionable
Invoice No.	580		800 Coco Drive
			Coconut Grove, FL 33133

Quantity	Description	Unit Price	Amount
50	Spin Bike Lubricator	20.00	1,000.00
5	Spin Bike I	2,000.00	10,000.00
2	Spin Bike II	2,400.00	4,800.00
	F.O.B. Shipping Point		
	Freight Charges		1,100.00
	Total		16,900.00

Form 36

Fit & Fashionable

800 Coco Drive, Coconut Grove, FL 33133

Interoffice Memo

To: Bookkeeper **Date:** April 18, 20--

Please issue checks for the following:

- Fit & Fab Health Products for $4,267.90 in payment of its invoice of April 6 less the return of April 11 and the discount.
- Muscles R_X Distributors in payment of its invoice of March 21 for $53,200.00.

Marty Chavez

Form 37

Sunshine Gazette
10332 S.W. 104 St., Miami, FL 33186

REC'D April 18

DATE April 17, 20--

TERMS Net Cash

SOLD TO Fit & Fashionable
800 Coco Drive
Coconut Grove, FL 33133

April 15 Advertisement $185.00

Please pay – MC

Form 38

The Sun Set Recreation Centers
50 Snapper Creek Dr.
Sunset, FL 33173

REC'D April 18

4524

April 17 20 --

Pay to the Order of Fit & Fashionable $ 20,933.68

Twenty thousand, nine hundred thirty-three and 68/100---- **Dollars**

(For Classroom Use Only)

LINCOLN FEDERAL SAVINGS BANK

For 4/8 Inv. Less 4/9 Credit Memo #107 Less 2% Discount

Chris E. Lee

⑆ 900 002230⑆ 25⑈011⑈ 4524

Form 39

Fit & Fashionable

800 Coco Drive, Coconut Grove, FL 33133

CREDIT MEMO NO. 108

Date: 4/19/20--
For: Our Invoice of April 16
We credit your account as follows:

Sold To: Miami Health Club
8050 S.W. 8th Street
Miami, FL 33130

Quantity	Item	Unit Cost	Amount
10	Running Shorts	42.50	425.00
	Total		425.00

Accounting Department Copy — For Office Use Only

Cost of Merchandise Sold 304.00 | *Sale net of 2% discount 416.50*

Form 40

Rockdale Gym
162 S. Dixie Hwy.
Rockdale, FL 33157

REC'D April 19

3644

April 18 20 --

Pay to the Order of Fit & Fashionable $ 13,373.86

Thirteen thousand, three hundred seventy-three and 86/100--- **Dollars**

(For Classroom Use Only)

Columbia Federal Savings Bank

For 4/10 Inv. #305 Less 2% Discount

Mayla Rodriguez

⑆ 5 00800⑆ 336⑈121⑈ 3644

Form 41

Fit & Fashionable

800 Coco Drive, Coconut Grove, FL 33133

Interoffice Memo

To: Bookkeeper

Date: April 20, 20--

Please issue a check to me for $231.00 for customer entertainment. Charge to Miscellaneous Selling Expense.

Marty Chavez

Form 42

FIZZY-CAL NETWORK

45 Caribbean Avenue

Los Angeles, CA 90001

REC'D April 20

DATE: April 19, 20--

SOLD TO: Fit & Fashionable
800 Coco Drive
Coconut Grove, FL 33133

INVOICE NO.: 3735

SHIPPED VIA: Custom Trucking

TERMS: Net 30

QUANTITY	DESCRIPTION	UNIT PRICE	AMOUNT
5	Exercise Bike Advanced	720.00	3,600.00
50	Cycling Shorts	30.50	1,525.00
1	Display Rack	225.00	225.00
	Charge to Store Supplies	TOTAL	5,350.00

Form 43

South Miami Bank

63-22
631

Date April 20, 20--

Fit & Fashionable
800 Coco Drive, Coconut Grove, FL 33133

Cost of Merchandise Sold $19,292.80

⑆74 00 2044⑆ 2⑈099 1⑈

COPY

	$	Cents
Cash	20,645	00
Checks 04-12	1,500	00
104-36	75	00
104-48	830	00
104-96	2,450	00
104-98	1,520	00
Cash Sales		
April 15-20		
Total	27,020	00

Form 44

South Miami Bank

63-22
631

Date

Fit & Fashionable
800 Coco Drive, Coconut Grove, FL 33133

⑆74 00 2044⑆ 2⑈099 1⑈

	$	Cents
Cash		
Checks		
Total		

Form 45

HeartFit Enterprises
15 Brickell Ave. #150
Miami, FL 33129

REC'D April 22

Date: April 21, 20--
Shipped Via: Boyd Trucking
Terms: Net 30
Invoice No: 6516

Sold To: Fit & Fashionable
800 Coco Drive
Coconut Grove, FL 33133

Quantity	Description	Unit Price	Amount
25	Heart Rate Pocket Monitor	36.00	900.00
25	Heart Rate Fitness Monitor	40.00	1,000.00
25	Heart Rate Watch	44.00	1,100.00
20	Drug Test Kit	20.00	400.00
	Total		3,400.00

Form 46

FIZZY-CAL NETWORK
45 Caribbean Avenue
Los Angeles, CA 90001

REC'D April 22

DATE: April 22, 20--

SOLD TO: Fit & Fashionable
800 Coco Drive
Coconut Grove, FL 33133

INVOICE NO.: 3812
SHIPPED VIA: Custom Trucking
TERMS: Net 30

QUANTITY	DESCRIPTION	UNIT PRICE	AMOUNT
5	Stair Climber Pro	2,160.00	10,800.00
		TOTAL	10,800.00

Form 47

Fit & Fashionable

800 Coco Drive, Coconut Grove, FL 33133

Date: 4/23/20--
Invoice: 307
Shipped Via: Speedy Trucking

Terms: 2/10, n/30

Sold To: All Access Fitness Centers
1 South Park Blvd.
South Miami, FL 33143

Quantity	Item	Unit Cost	Amount
5	Unisex DryFit Shirts	33.60	168.00
8	Athletic Shoes	119.99	959.92
3	Spin Bike II	3,360.00	10,080.00
7	Rowing Kit Portable	125.00	875.00
5	Cycling Bike II	393.75	1,968.75
	Total		14,051.67

Accounting Department Copy — For Office Use Only

Cost of Merchandise Sold 10,040.00	*Sale net of 2% discount 13,770.64*

Form 48

Sports Magic Warehouse

246 Santa Monica Blvd.
Santa Monica, CA 90403

REC'D April 24

Date April 23, 20--
Sold To Fit & Fashionable
800 Coco Drive
Coconut Grove, FL 33133

Shipped Via Our Truck
Terms Net 30
Invoice No. 670

Quantity	Description	Unit Price	Amount
1	Spin Bike IV	2,400.00	2,400.00
	Total		2,400.00

Form 49

Fit & Fashionable

800 Coco Drive, Coconut Grove, FL 33133

Interoffice Memo

To: Bookkeeper **Date:** April 24, 20--

Please issue a check for $287.00 to Miami Cleaning Services for cleaning supplies. Charge to Miscellaneous Administrative Expense.

Marty Chavez

Form 50

HeartFit Enterprises
15 Brickell Ave. #150
Miami, FL 33129

REC'D April 25

CREDIT MEMO: CM#114

Date: April 23, 20--

Sold To: Fit & Fashionable
800 Coco Drive
Coconut Grove, FL 33133

Quantity	Description	Unit Price	Amount
20	Drug Test Kit	20.00	400.00
	On our invoice dated April 21, 20--		
	Total		400.00

Form 51

Fit & Fashionable

800 Coco Drive, Coconut Grove, FL 33133

Date: 4/25/20--
Invoice: 308
Shipped Via: Express Trucking

Terms: 2/10, n/30

Sold To: Cory's Gym in the Grove
20 Main Highway
Coconut Grove, FL 33133

Quantity	Item	Unit Cost	Amount
4	Cycling Bike I	315.75	1,263.00
2	Exercise Bike Advanced	1,025.00	2,050.00
30	Cycling Shorts	42.79	1,283.70
6	Running Shorts	42.50	255.00
10	Running Tanks	27.25	272.50
5	Unisex DryFit Shirts	33.60	168.00
	Total		5,292.20

Accounting Department Copy — For Office Use Only

Cost of Merchandise Sold 3,780.00 | *Sale net of 2% discount 5,186.36*

Form 52

Fit & Fashionable

800 Coco Drive, Coconut Grove, FL 33133

Interoffice Memo

To: Bookkeeper

Date: April 26, 20--

Please issue a check to Payroll for $13,000.00 for biweekly salaries: Sales Salaries, $8,000.00; Office Salaries, $5,000.00.

Marty Chavez

Form 53

Fit & Fashionable

800 Coco Drive, Coconut Grove, FL 33133

Date: 4/26/20--
Invoice: 309
Shipped Via: Express Trucking

Terms: 2/10, n/30

Sold To: Body Excellence Fitness Club
9 Key Biscayne Ave., Suite 100
Key Biscayne, FL 33149

Quantity	Item	Unit Cost	Amount
2	Exercise Bike Advanced	1,025.00	2,050.00
10	Heart Rate Fitness Monitor	62.50	625.00
10	Heart Rate Watch Digital	68.75	687.50
15	Unisex DryFit Shirts	33.60	504.00
	Total		3,866.50

Accounting Department Copy — For Office Use Only

Cost of Merchandise Sold 2,640.00	Sale net of 2% discount 3,789.17

Form 54

Miami Water Supply Department

ACCOUNT NO.: 684 2563 A

DATE: April 24, 20--

TO: Fit & Fashionable
800 Coco Drive
Coconut Grove, FL 33133

REC'D April 27

Charge to Misc. Admin. Expense
Please pay
MC

METER READINGS:

Present 550
Previous 212
Consumption 338

CHARGES:

Water 176.00
Sewage 164.00
Total 340.00

AMOUNT DUE $340.00

Form 55

Fit & Fashionable

800 Coco Drive, Coconut Grove, FL 33133

Interoffice Memo

To: Bookkeeper **Date:** April 27, 20--

Please issue the following checks:

- To Alexus Fitness for $13,865.00 in payment of its invoice received April 1
- To me for $2,500.00 for personal use

Marty Chavez

Form 56

Florida Telephone

REC'D April 27

DATE: April 27, 20--

TO: Fit & Fashionable
800 Coco Drive
Coconut Grove, FL 33133

Local Service	$232.00
Long Distance Calls	380.00
TOTAL	$612.00

Charge Misc. Admin. Exp. $204.00
Charge Misc. Selling Exp. $408.00

Please Pay – MC

Form 57

MIA GAS & ELECTRIC

REC'D April 29

Billed To: Fit & Fashionable
800 Coco Drive
Coconut Grove, FL 33133

Account No.: 7213T

Next Reading: May 28

Area: 3

Terms: Net

Charge to Misc. Admin. Expense

	GAS	**ELECTRIC**
Reading	7,320	2,750
Days	30	30
Quantity	524	1,050

CURRENT CHARGES:

Gas $133.65
Electric $226.35

BALANCE DUE $360.00

Please pay – MC

Form 58

Fit & Fashionable

800 Coco Drive, Coconut Grove, FL 33133

Interoffice Memo

To: Bookkeeper

Date: April 30, 20--

Please issue a check for $700.00 to South Miami Bank in payment of interest on the note payable for April.

Marty Chavez

Form 59

Blue Water Enterprises
5501 Duval Street
Key West, FL 33040

REC'D April 30

183

April 27 20 --

Pay to the Order of Fit & Fashionable $ 3,060.00

Three thousand sixty and 00/100---------------------------- **Dollars**

(For Classroom Use Only)

Lincoln National

For $3,000 note + $60 interest

George Peterson

⑆ 76 88003⑆ 25⑈0791⑈ 183

Form 60

South Miami Bank

63-22
631

Date April 30, 20--

Fit &
Fashionable
800 Coco Drive, Coconut Grove, FL 33133

Cost of Merchandise Sold *$19,099.20*

⑆ 74 002044⑆ 2⑈099 1⑈

COPY

	$	Cents
Cash	24,858	00
Checks 92-104	3,422	00
Cash Sales		
April 22-30		
Total	28,280	00

Form 61

South Miami Bank

63-22
631

Date ______________________

Fit &
Fashionable
800 Coco Drive, Coconut Grove, FL 33133

⑆74 002044⑆ 2⑈099 1⑈

	$	Cents
Cash		
Checks		
Total		

Note: After the documents in Forms 1–60 are recorded in the appropriate journals, continue with the instructions on page 2 of Booklet 1.

Fit & Fashionable

800 Coco Drive, Coconut Grove, FL 33133

NARRATIVE OF TRANSACTIONS

Record the following transactions in the appropriate journals.

April 1 Purchased merchandise on account from Alexus Fitness Connection, $13,865.00. Terms are n/30.

1 Sold merchandise on account, Invoice No. 301, to Miami Health Club for the net amount of $5,301.60. The Cost of Merchandise Sold is $3,864.00.

Credit terms for all sales on account are 2/10, n/30. Credit sales are recorded net of the 2% discount assuming customers will take the discount. Fit & Fashionable uses a perpetual inventory system and therefore records the cost of merchandise sold as well as the sale.

1 Issued Check No. 2201 for $14,268.80 to Alexus Fitness Connection in payment of its invoice of March 6.

2 Received a check for $14,406.00 from Body Excellence Fitness Club in payment of our invoice of March 27 for $14,700.00, less discount.

2 Issued Check No. 2202 for $5,700.00 to Harvey Insurance Company as a prepayment of insurance for a 12-month policy.

3 Issued Check No. 2203 for $46,480.00 to Fizzy-Cal Network in payment of its invoice of March 7 (no discount).

3 Sold merchandise on account, Invoice No. 302, to All Access Fitness Centers for the net amount of $9,364.29. The Cost of Merchandise Sold is $6,825.00.

3 Received a check from Cory's Gym in the Grove for $12,348.00 in payment of our invoice of March 27.

April 4 Issued Check No. 2204 for $14,000.00 to HeartFit Enterprises in payment of its invoice of March 28.

4 Received a check for $6,174.00 from The Sun Set Recreation Centers in payment of our invoice of March 8.

5 Sold merchandise on account, Invoice No. 303, to Westwood Boxing Gym for the net amount of $27,306.48. The Cost of Merchandise Sold is $19,903.68.

5 Purchased merchandise on account from Sports Magic Warehouse, $49,519.75. Terms are n/30.

6 Cash sales for April 1–6 were $26,600.00. The Cost of Merchandise Sold is $18,024.00.

Reminder: Record the following separate deposits in the checkbook register: the $26,600.00 of cash sales and the total of the checks received as payments on account this week.

8 Received a check for $8,232.00 from Westwood Boxing Gym in payment of our invoice of March 29 for $8,400.00, less discount.

8 Purchased merchandise on account from Fit & Fab Health Products, $5,230.00, terms 2/10, n/30. Record this purchase net of the discount.

8 Sold merchandise on account, Invoice No. 304, to The Sun Set Recreation Centers for the net amount of $21,756.88. The Cost of Merchandise Sold is $15,858.00.

April 8 Received a check for $10,976.00 from Pine Bay Fitness Club in payment of our invoice of March 30.

9 Purchased the following on account from Fizzy-Cal Network: display (charge to Store Supplies), $1,800.00; merchandise, $9,600.00. Total: $11,400.00. Terms are n/30.

9 Issued Credit Memorandum No. 107 to The Sun Set Recreation Centers for merchandise returned on Invoice No. 304 of April 8 for the discounted price of $823.20. The Cost of Merchandise Sold is $600.00.

10 Issued Check No. 2205 for $175.00 to Marty Chavez for customer entertainment (charge to Miscellaneous Selling Expense).

10 Sold merchandise on account, Invoice No. 305, to Rockdale Gym for the net amount of $13,373.86. The Cost of Merchandise Sold is $9,412.00.

11 Received Credit Memorandum No. 432 from Fit & Fab Health Products for merchandise returned, $875.00. Record this return net of the discount, $857.50.

11 Received a check for $300.00 from SupplyMax for return of store supplies that were originally purchased for cash.

11 Received a check for $5,301.60 from Miami Health Club in payment of Invoice No. 301.

12 Received a check for $9,364.29 from All Access Fitness Centers in payment of Invoice No. 302.

13 Issued Check No. 2206 for $13,000.00 to Payroll for biweekly salaries: sales salaries, $8,000.00; office salaries, $5,000.00.

13 Cash sales for April 8–13 were $36,120.00. The Cost of Merchandise Sold is $24,910.80.

Reminder: Record the following separate deposits in the checkbook register: the $36,120.00 of cash sales and the total of the checks received as payments on account this week.

April 15 Received a check for $27,306.48 from Westwood Boxing Gym in payment of Invoice No. 303.

16 Purchased the following items on account from Alexus Fitness Connection: merchandise inventory, $9,180.00; miscellaneous selling expense (display cases), $675.00; store supplies (promotion pack), $250.00. Total: $10,105.00. Terms are n/30.

16 Sold merchandise on account, Invoice No. 306, to Miami Health Club for the net amount of $5,649.80. The Cost of Merchandise Sold is $4,115.20.

17 Issued Check No. 2207 for $4,200.00 to Marty Chavez for personal use.

17 Issued Check No. 2208 for $441.00 to *U.S. Health & Fitness Magazine* for an advertisement.

17 Purchased merchandise on account from Sports Magic Warehouse, $16,900.00. Terms are n/30.

18 Issued Check No. 2209 for $4,267.90 to Fit & Fab Health Products in payment of its invoice of April 6 less the return of April 11 and the discount.

18 Issued Check No. 2210 for $53,200.00 to Muscles R_X Distributors in payment of its invoice of March 21.

18 Issued Check No. 2211 for $185.00 to *Sunshine Gazette* for an advertisement in the April 15 edition.

18 Received a check for $20,933.68 from The Sun Set Recreation Centers in payment of Invoice No. 304 less the return of April 9 and the discount.

19 Issued Credit Memorandum No. 108 to Miami Health Club for merchandise returned on our April 16 invoice for the discounted price of $416.50. The Cost of Merchandise Sold is $304.00.

19 Received a check for $13,373.86 from Rockdale Gym in payment of Invoice No. 305.

April 20 Issued Check No. 2212 for $231.00 to Marty Chavez for customer entertainment (charge to Miscellaneous Selling Expense).

20 Purchased the following on account from Fizzy-Cal Network: merchandise, $5,125.00; store supplies, $225.00. Total, $5,350.00. Terms are n/30.

20 Cash sales for April 15–20 were $27,020.00. The Cost of Merchandise Sold is $19,292.80.

Reminder: Record the following separate deposits in the checkbook register: the $27,020.00 of cash sales and the total of the checks received as payments on account this week.

22 Purchased merchandise on account from HeartFit Enterprises, $3,400.00. Terms are n/30.

22 Purchased merchandise on account from Fizzy-Cal Network, $10,800.00. Terms are n/30.

23 Sold merchandise on account, Invoice No. 307, to All Access Fitness Centers for the net amount of $13,770.64. The Cost of Merchandise Sold is $10,040.00.

24 Purchased merchandise on account from Sports Magic Warehouse, $2,400.00. Terms are n/30.

24 Issued Check No. 2213 for $287.00 to Miami Cleaning Services for cleaning supplies (charge to Miscellaneous Administrative Expense).

25 Received Credit Memorandum No. 114 from HeartFit Enterprises for merchandise returned, $400.00. There was no discount.

25 Sold merchandise on account, Invoice No. 308, to Cory's Gym in the Grove for the net amount of $5,186.36. The Cost of Merchandise Sold is $3,780.00.

April 26 Issued Check No. 2214 for $13,000.00 to Payroll for biweekly salaries: sales salaries, $8,000.00; office salaries, $5,000.00.

26 Sold merchandise on account, Invoice No. 309, to Body Excellence Fitness Club for the net amount of $3,789.17. The Cost of Merchandise Sold is $2,640.00.

27 Issued Check No. 2215 to Miami Water Supply Department for $340.00 in payment of the water bill for the month (charge to Miscellaneous Administrative Expense).

27 Issued Check No. 2216 for $13,865.00 to Alexus Fitness Connection in payment of its invoice received April 20.

27 Issued Check No. 2217 for $2,500.00 to Marty Chavez for personal use.

29 Issued Check No. 2218 to Florida Telephone for $612.00 in payment of the telephone bill for the month (charge $204.00 to Miscellaneous Administrative Expense and $408.00 to Miscellaneous Selling Expense).

29 Issued Check No. 2219 to MIA Gas & Electric for $360.00 in payment of the gas and electric bill for the month (charge to Misc. Admin. Expense).

30 Issued Check No. 2220 for $700.00 to South Miami Bank in payment of interest on a note payable for April.

30 Received a check for $3,060.00 from Blue Water Enterprises in payment of a $3,000.00 note receivable plus $60.00 interest earned.

30 Cash sales for April 22–30 were $28,280.00. The Cost of Merchandise Sold is $19,099.20.

Reminder: Record the following separate deposits in the checkbook register: the $28,280.00 of cash sales and the total of the checks received as payments on account this week.

Note: After all the transactions are recorded in the appropriate journals, continue with the instructions on page 2 of Booklet 1.

NOTES

NOTES